D1473293

WASHINGTON
AND
LINCOLN
IN POETRY

Carnegie Library School
Association

WASHINGTON AND LINCOLN IN POETRY

POEMS CHOSEN BY A
COMMITTEE OF THE
CARNEGIE LIBRARY
SCHOOL ASSOCIATION

NEW YORK
THE H. W. WILSON COMPANY
1927

Published January, 1927

Printed in the United States of America

PREFACE

As in the other booklets of this series, the poems are printed on one side of the page only so that they may be mounted and used separately if desired. The poems are within a child's comprehension.

The proceeds derived from the publication of these booklets are used to increase the Student Loan Fund of the Association.

This booklet is the last of a series of holiday poetry booklets compiled by a poetry committee of Alumnae of the Carnegie Library School. The committee consists of: Dorothy Grout of East Cleveland, Ohio; Mary Wilkinson of Baltimore, Maryland; Jasmine Britton of Los Angeles, California; Grace Darling of Boston, Massachusetts; Alice Stoeltzing of Pittsburgh, Pennsylvania; and Dorothy Hayes of Hinsdale, Illinois.

Mildred P. Harrington,
Chairman of the Poetry Committee,
Carnegie Library School Association.

19621

CONTENTS

WASHINGTON

CONTENTS—*Continued*

LINCOLN

CONTENTS—*Continued*

AT THE TOMB OF WASHINGTON

Here let the brows be bared
 Before the land's great son,
He who undaunted dared,
 Our Washington!

From dole, despair and doubt,
 Deceit and enmity,
He led us up and out
 To Victory.

A Pharos in the night,
 A pillar in the dawn,
By his inspiring light
 May we fare on!

Day upon hastening day
 Still let us reverence him;
Fame, never, never may
 His laurels dim!

Clinton Scollard.

Included by permission of the author.

EPITAPH ON WASHINGTON

The defender of his country,—the founder of liberty,
The friend of man,
History and tradition are explored in vain
For a parallel to his character.
In the annals of modern greatness
He stands alone;
And the noblest names of antiquity
Lose their lustre in his presence.
Born the benefactor of mankind,
He united all the greatness necessary
To an illustrious career.
Nature made him great,
He made himself virtuous.
Called by his Country to the defense of her liberties,
He triumphantly vindicated the rights of humanity,
And, on the pillars of National Independence,
Laid the foundation of a great Republic.

Twice invested with Supreme Magistracy
By the unanimous vote of a free people,
He surpassed, in the Cabinet,
The glories of the field,
And, voluntarily resigning the scepter and the sword,
Retired to the shades of private life;
A spectacle so new, and so sublime,
Was contemplated with profoundest admiration,
And the name of Washington,
Adding new lustre to humanity,
Resounded to the remotest regions of the earth.
Magnanimous in youth,
Glorious through life,
Great in death;
His highest ambition, the happiness of mankind;
His noblest victory, the conquest of himself,
Bequeathing to posterity the inheritance of his fame.
And building his monument in the hearts of his Countrymen,—
He lived—the ornament of the Eighteenth Century;
He died, regretted by a mourning world.

2

GEORGE WASHINGTON

Only a baby, fair and small,
    Like many another baby son,
Whose smiles and tears come swift at call;
Who ate, and slept, and grew, that's all—
    The infant Washington.

Only a boy, like other boys,
    With tasks and studies, sports and fun;
Fond of his books and games and toys;
Living his childish griefs and joys—
    The little Washington.

Only a lad, awkward and shy,
    Skilled in handling a horse or gun;
Mastering knowledge that, by and by,
Should aid him in duties great and high—
    The youthful Washington.

Only a man of finest bent,
    Hero of battles fought and won;
Surveyor, General, President,
Who served his country, and dies content—
    The patriot Washington.

Only—ah! what was the secret, then,
    Of his being America's honored son?
Why was he famed above other men?
His name upon every tongue and pen—
    The illustrious Washington.

A mighty brain, a will to endure,
    Passions subdued, a slave to none,
A heart that was brave and strong and sure,
A soul that was noble and great and pure,
A faith in God that was held secure—
    This was George Washington.

                Anonymous.

GEORGE WASHINGTON

This was the man God gave us when the hour
Proclaimed the dawn of Liberty begun;
Who dared a deed, and died when it was done,
Patient in triumph, temperate in power,—
Not striving like the Corsican to tower
To heaven, nor like great Philip's greater son
To win the world and weep for worlds unwon,
Or lose the star to revel in the flower.
The lives that serve the eternal verities
Alone do mould mankind, Pleasure and pride
Sparkle awhile and perish, as the spray
Smoking across the crests of the cavernous seas
Is impotent to hasten or delay
The everlasting surges of the tide.

John Hall Ingham.

INSCRIPTION AT MOUNT VERNON

Washington, the brave, the wise, the good.
Supreme in war, in council, and in peace.
Valiant without ambition, discreet without fear,
           confident without presumption.
In disaster calm; in success, moderate; in all, himself.
The hero, the patriot, the Christian.
The father of nations, the friend of mankind,
Who, when he had won all, renounced all, and sought
    in the bosom of his family and of nature,
    retirement, and in the hope of religion,
    immortality.

Anonymous.

A MAN!

About his brow the laurel and the bay
    Was often wreathed,—on this our memory dwells,—
Upon whose bier in reverence today
    We lay these immortelles.

His was a vital, virile, warrior soul;
    If force were needed, he exalted force;
Unswerving as the pole star to the pole,
    He held his righteous course.

He smote at Wrong, if he believed it Wrong,
    As did the Knight, with stainless accolade;
He stood for Right, unfalteringly strong,
    Forever unafraid.

With somewhat of the savant and the sage,
    He was, when all is said and sung, a man,
The flower imperishable of this valient age,—
    A true American!

Clinton Scollard.

Included by permission of the author and The Sun.

MOUNT VERNON, THE HOME OF
WASHINGTON

There dwelt the Man, the flower of human kind,
Whose visage mild bespoke his nobler mind.

There dwelt the Soldier, who his sword ne'er drew
But in a righteous cause, to Freedom true.

There dwelt the Hero, who ne'er killed for fame,
Yet gained more glory than a Caesar's name.

There dwelt the Statesman, who, devoid of art,
Gave soundest counsels from an upright heart;

And, O Columbia, by thy sons caressed,
There dwelt the Father of the realms he blessed;
Who no wish felt to make his mighty praise,
Like other chiefs, the means himself to raise;
But there retiring, breathed in pure renown,
And felt a grandeur that disdained a crown.

William Day.

OLD SONG WRITTEN DURING WASHINGTON'S LIFE

Americans, rejoice;
While songs employ the voice,
  Let trumpets sound.
The thirteen stripes display
In flags and streamers gay,
'Tis Washington's birthday,
  Let joy abound.

Long may he live to see
This land of liberty
  Flourish in peace;
Long may he live to prove
A grateful people's love,
And late to heaven remove,
  Where joys ne'er cease.

Fill the glass to the brink,
Washington's health we'll drink,
  'Tis his birthday.
Glorious deeds he has done,
By him our cause is won,
Long live great Washington!
  Huzza! Huzza!

                    Anonymous.

THE SHIP OF STATE

Thou, too, sail on, O Ship of State!
Sail on, O Union, strong and great!
Humanity with all its fears,
With all the hopes of future years,
Is hanging breathless on thy fate!
We know what master laid thy keel,
What Workmen wrought thy ribs of steel,
Who made each mast, and sail, and rope,
What anvils rang, what hammers beat,
In what a forge and what a heat
Were shaped the anchors of thy hope!
Fear not each sudden sound and shock,
'Tis of the wave and not the rock;
'Tis but the flapping of the sail,
And not a rent made by the gale!
In spite of rock and tempest's roar,
In spite of false lights on the shore,
Sail on, nor fear to breast the sea!
Our hearts, our hopes, our prayers, our tears,
Our faith triumphant o'er our fears,
Are all with thee,—are all with thee!

Henry Wadsworth Longfellow.

Included by permission of Houghton, Mifflin Company.

TRIBUTE TO WASHINGTON

Great without pomp, without ambition brave,
Proud, not to conquer fellow-men, but save;
Friend to the weak, a foe to none but those
Who plan their greatness on their brethren's woes;
Aw'd by no titles—undefil'd by lust—
Free without faction—obstinately just;
Warm'd by religion's sacred, genuine ray,
That points to future bliss the unerring way;
Yet ne'er control'd by superstition's laws,
That worst of tyrants in the noblest cause.

From a London Newspaper.

UNION AND LIBERTY

Flag of the heroes who left us their glory,
   Borne through their battle-fields' thunder and flame,
Blazoned in song and illumined in story,
   Wave o'er us all, who inherit their fame!
     Up with our banner bright,
     Sprinkled with starry light,
   Spread its fair emblems from mountain to shore,
     While through the sounding sky
     Loud rings the Nation's cry,—
UNION AND LIBERTY! ONE EVERMORE!

Light of our firmament, guide of our Nation,
   Pride of her children, honored afar,
Let the wide beams of thy full constellation
   Scatter each cloud that would darken a star!
     Up with our banner bright,
     Sprinkled with starry light,
   Spread its fair emblems from mountain to shore,
     While through the sounding sky
     Loud rings the Nation's cry,—
UNION AND LIBERTY! ONE EVERMORE!

Empire unsceptred! what foe shall assail thee,
   Bearing the standard of Liberty's van?
Think not the God of thy fathers shall fail thee,
   Striving with men for the birthright of man!
     Up with our banner bright,
     Sprinkled with starry light,
   Spread its fair emblems from mountain to shore,
     While through the sounding sky
     Loud rings the Nation's cry,—
UNION AND LIBERTY! ONE EVERMORE!

11

Yet, if by madness and treachery blighted,
  Dawns the dark hour when the sword thou must draw,
Then with the arms of thy million united,
  Smite the bold traitors to Freedom and Law!
    Up with our banner bright,
    Sprinkled with starry light,
  Spread its fair emblems from mountain to shore,
    While through the sounding sky
    Loud rings the Nation's cry,—
UNION AND LIBERTY! ONE EVERMORE!

Lord of the Universe! shield us and guide us,
  Trusting Thee always, through shadow and sun!
Thou hast united us, who shall divide us?
  Keep us, oh keep us the MANY IN ONE!
    Up with our banner bright,
    Sprinkled with starry light,
  Spread its fair emblems from mountain to shore,
    While through the sounding sky,
    Loud rings the Nation's cry,—
UNION AND LIBERTY! ONE EVERMORE!

Oliver W. Holmes

Included by permission of Houghton, Mifflin Company.

WASHINGTON

Where may the wearied eye repose
    When gazing on the Great;
Where neither guilty glory glows,
    Nor despicable state?
Yes—one—the first—the last—the best—
The Cincinnatus of the West,
    Whom envy dare not hate,
Bequeath the name of Washington,
To make men blush there was but one!

Lord Byron.

WASHINGTON

Soldier and statesman, rarest unison;
High-poised example of great duties done
Simply as breathing, a world's honors worn
As life's indifferent gifts to all men born;
Dumb for himself, unless it were to God,
But for his barefoot soldiers eloquent,
Tramping the snow to corral where they trod,
Held by his awe in hollow-eyed content;
Modest, yet firm as Nature's self; unblamed
Save by the men his nobler temper shamed;
Never seduced through show of present good
By other than unsetting lights to steer
New-trimmed in Heaven, nor than his steadfast mood
More steadfast, far from rashness as from fear;
Rigid, but with himself first, grasping still
In swerveless poise the wave-beat helm of will;
Not honored then or now because he wooed
The popular voice, but that he still withstood;
Broad-minded, higher-souled, there is but one
Who was all this and ours, and all men's,—Washington.

James Russell Lowell.
(From "Under the Elm")

Included by permission of Houghton, Mifflin Company.

WASHINGTON

It seems so simple now, that life of thine,
To us who from these turgid days look back,
As mariners from 'neath a stormy wrack
Peer out and see a verdant island shine
Behind them, where the storm has left no sign
Save freshness and new glory in its track;
To us, who midst sunk rocks still turn and tack,
So seem thy days all happy, free and fine.

Yet, wert thou here, wouldst not thy piercing gaze,
Thy steady hand and strong, compelling will,
Unravel the mixt strands of good and ill
That so perplex? In youth through wildwood maze
Thy skill surveyed clear paths; and later, lo!
The way was straight because thou mad'st it so.

Geraldine Meyrich.

Included by permission of Overland Monthly.

WASHINGTON
(*From the "Columbian Ode"*)

When foolish kings, at odds with swift-paced Time,
    Would strike that banner down,
A nobler knight than ever writ or rhyme
Has starred with fame's bright crown
Through armed hosts bore it free to float on high
Beyond the clouds, a light that cannot die.
    Ah, hero of our younger race,
    Strong builder of a temple new,
    Ruler who sought no lordly place,
    Warrior who sheathed the sword he drew!—
    Lover of men, who saw afar
    A world unmarred by want or war,
    Who knew the path, and yet forbore
    To tread till all men should implore;
    Who saw the light, and led the way
    Where the grey world might greet the day;
    Father and leader, prophet sure,
    Whose will in vast works shall endure.
How shall we praise him on this day of days,
Great son of fame who has no need of praise?

How shall we praise him? Open wide the doors
Of the fair temple whose broad base he laid.
Through its white halls a shadowy cavalcade
Of heroes moves on unresounding floors—
Men whose brawned arms upraised these columns high,
And reared the towers that vanish in the sky—
The strong who, having wrought, can never die.

And here, leading a gallant host, comes one
Who held a warring nation in his heart;
Who knew love's agony, but had no part
In love's delight; whose mighty task was done
Through blood and tears that we might walk in joy,
And this day's rapture feel no sad alloy.
Around him heirs of bliss, whose bright brows wear
Palm-leaves amid their laurels ever fair.

16

Gaily they come, as though the drum
Beat out the call their glad hearts knew so well;
Brothers once more, dear as of yore,
Who in a noble conflict nobly fell.
Their blood washed pure yon banner in the sky,
And quenched the brands under these arches high—
The brave who, having fought, can never die.

Harriet Monroe.

Revised by the author.
Included by permission of the author and The Macmillan Company.

WASHINGTON

Thou gallant Chief whose glorious name
Doth still adorn the Book of Fame:
Whose deeds shall live while freemen prize
The cause for which the Patriot dies,
Long to Columbia may'st thou be
The beacon light of Liberty.

Rev. Denis O'Crowley.

WASHINGTON

Our Nation's birth gave history your name,
　　Recording on its pages your great deeds.
No hesitation marred when duty came,
　　No clouds obscured from you your country's needs.
Pure were the thoughts you planted in man's heart,
　　Nor is your harvest fully garnered yet;
Still grows and thrives the tree that had its start,
　　In hallowed ground with honest purpose wet.
Each passing day your wisdom is revealed,
　　Each added year some richer promise gives;
Your presence led our fathers in the field,
　　Your spirit leads us still to that which lives
In Liberty and Peace, for which you fought
　　To gain Eternity, the goal you sought.

John A. Prentice.

ncluded by permission of Overland Monthly.

WASHINGTON

O noble brow, so wise in thought!
O heart, so true! O soul unbought!
O eye, so keen to pierce the night
And guide the "ship of state" aright!
O life so simple, grand and free,
The humblest still may turn to thee.
O king, uncrowned! O prince of men!
When shall we see thy like again?
The century, just passed away,
Has felt the impress of thy sway,
While youthful hearts have stronger grown
And made thy patriot zeal their own.
In marble hall or lowly cot,
Thy name hath never been forgot.
The world itself is richer, far,
For the clear shining of a star.
And loyal hearts in years to run
Shall turn to thee, O Washington.

Mary Wingate.

WASHINGTON MONUMENT BY NIGHT

1

The stone goes straight.
A lean swimmer dives into night sky,
Into half-moon mist.

2

Two trees are coal black.
This is a great white ghost between.
It is cool to look at.
Strong men, strong women, come here.

3

Eight years is a long time
To be fighting all the time.

4

The republic is a dream.
Nothing happens unless first a dream.

5

The wind bit hard at Valley Forge one Christmas.
Soldiers tied rags on their feet.
Red footprints wrote on the snow. . .
. . . and stone shoots into stars here
. . . into half-moon mist to-night.

6

Tongues wrangled dark at a man.
He buttoned his overcoat and stood alone.
In a snowstorm, red hollyberries, thoughts,
      he stood alone.

7

Women said: He is lonely
. . . fighting . . . fighting . . . eight years. . .

8

The name of an iron man goes over the world.
It takes a long time to forget an iron man.

9

. . . .
. . . .

Carl Sandburg.

From "Slabs of the Sunburnt West."
Included by permission of the author and Harcourt, Brace and Company.

WASHINGTON'S BIRTHDAY

All honor to that day which long ago
    Gave birth to him who Freedom's cause espoused;
Who, by his ardor in the sacred fight,
    The fire and strength of patriots aroused;
Who knew no master, save that One divine
    Whose strength was his, who knew no fear, save one—
The fear of doing wrong!   All hail the day
    That gave to Freedom's cause George Washington.

Years come and go, and generations fall
    Into the dust. The world its heroes gives.
They step upon the stage, then pass away
    And are no more, but Freedom ever lives.
And while it lives, and while its banner bright
    Is upward flung into the golden sun,
Within the heart of every freeman's child
    Will live that honored name, George Washington.

Then honor to the day that gave him birth,
    For it is also Freedom's natal day.
Let all who worship Freedom's cause stand forth
    And to his memory their homage pay.
And let each loyal son the work take up—
    For, know ye, Freedom's work is never done—
And greater, grander, build the edifice
    Begun so long ago by Washington.

Arthur J. Burdick.

WASHINGTON'S MONUMENT

For him who sought his country's good
In plains of war, 'mid scenes of blood;
Spent the warm noon of life's bright day,
Who in the dubious battle's fray,
That to a world he might secure
Rights that forever shall endure,
     Rear the monument of fame!
     Deathless is the hero's name.

For him, who, when the war was done,
And victory sure, and freedom won,
Left glory's theatre, the field,
The olive branch of peace to wield;
And proved, when at the helm of state,
Though great in war, in peace as great;
     Rear the monument of fame!
     Deathless is the hero's name!

For him, whose worth, though unexpress'd,
Lives cherished in each freeman's breast,
Whose name, to patriot souls so dear,
Time's latest children shall revere,
Whose brave achievements praised shall be,
While beats one breast for liberty;
     Rear the monument of fame!
     Deathless is the hero's name!

But why for him vain marbles raise?
Can the cold sculpture speak his praise?
Illustrious shade! we can proclaim
Our gratitude, but not thy fame.
Long as Columbia shall be free,
She lives a monument of thee,
     And may she ever rise in fame,
     To honor thy immortal name!

Anonymous.

WASHINGTON'S TOMB

Would we could coin for thee new words of praise;
To call thee only great, is meaningless;
Thou didst the woes of humankind redress,
And the blest standard of our freedom raise;
Didst lead us safe o'er strange, untrodden ways,
And in thy life—that did all truth express—
Teach us thy cherished creed which we confess,
The equal rights of men to crown their days.
Thou didst not sleep in sound of city's toil;
The din of traffic, murmur of the mart,
Are far away; within thy native soil
We leave thee, heart of honor, Honor's heart;
Not in cathedral's gorgeous sculptured gloom,
But 'neath thy much loved stars, a fitter tomb.

Ruth Lawrence.

From "Colonial Verses" by Ruth Lawrence.
Included by permission of the author and Brentano's.

WASHINGTON'S VOW

How felt the land in every part
The strong throb of a nation's heart?
As its great leader gave, with reverent awe,
His pledge to Union, Liberty, and Law!

That pledge the heavens above him heard,
That vow the sleep of centuries stirred.
In world-wide wonder listening peoples bent
Their gaze on Freedom's great experiment.

. . . . .

Thank God! the people's choice was just!
The one man equal to his trust.
Wise without lore, and without weakness good,
Calm in the strength of flawless rectitude.

. . . . .

Our first and best—his ashes lie
Beneath his own Virginia sky.
Forgive, forget, oh! true and just and brave,
The storm that swept above thy sacred grave.

. . . . .

Then let the sovereign millions where
Our banner floats in sun and air,
From the warm palm-lands to Alaska's cold,
Repeat with us the pledge, a century old!

John Greenleaf Whittier.

Included by permission of Houghton, Mifflin Company.

YOUNG WASHINGTON
(The Embassy to the French Forts, 1753)

Tie the moccasin, bind the pack,
Sling your rifle across your back,
Up! and follow the mountain track,
    Tread the Indian Trail.
North and west is the road we fare
Toward the forts of the Frenchmen, where
"Peace or War!" is the word we bear,
    Life and Death in the scale.

The leaves of October are dry on the ground,
The sheaves of Virginia are gathered and bound,
Her fallows are glad with the cry of the hound,
    The partridges whirr in the fern;
But deep are the forests and keen are the foes
Where Monongahela in wilderness flows;
We've labors and perils and torrents and snows
    To conquer before we return.

Hall and council-room, farm and chase,
Coat of scarlet and frill of lace
All are excellent things in place;
    Joy in these if ye can.
Mine be hunting-shirt, knife and gun,
Camp aglow on the sheltered run,
Friend and foe in the checkered sun;
    That's the life for a man!

Arthur Guiterman.

Revised by the author.
From *"I Sing the Pioneer,"* copyright 1926, by E. P. Dutton & Company. *Included by permission of the author.*

26

ABRAHAM LINCOLN

ABRAHAM LINCOLN

Born in a hovel, trained in Hardship's school,
He rose sublime, a conqueror over all.
His life of labor, thought and burden-bearing
Brought forth his kingly qualities of soul.
Upon his lofty brow he wore those crowns
Which only come with suffering and toil,
The crowns of wisdom, strength and God-like love
For all mankind, both enemies and friends.
His spirit still is with us in our need;
His work goes on increasing through all time.

A. S. Ames.

Included by permission of the Palmer Company, Publishers.

ABRAHAM LINCOLN

Whence came this man? As if on the wings
    Of the winds of God that blew!
He moved, undaunted, mid captains and kings,
    And, not having learned, he knew!
Was he son of the soil, or child of the sky?
    Or, pray, was he both? Ah me!
How little they dreamed, as the storm rolled nigh,
    What he was, and was to be!

When trembled the lamps of hope, or quite
    Blew out in that furious gale,
He drew his light from the Larger Light
    Above him that did not fail:
Heaven-led, all trials and perils among,
    As unto some splendid goal
He fared right onward, unflinching—this strong,
    God-gifted, heroic soul!

We know him now—how noble his part,
    And how clear was his vision then!
With the firmest hand and the kindliest heart
    Of them all—this master of men!
Of the pride of power or the lust of pelf,
    Oh, never a taint we find:
He lost himself in the larger self
    Of his country and all mankind.

There are those called great, or good, by right,
    But as long as the long roll is,
Not many the names, with the double light
    Of greatness and goodness, like his.
Thrice happy the nation that holds him dear
    Who never can wholly die,
Never cease to bestow of his counsel and cheer,
    As the perilous years go by!

For after the trumpets have ceased to blow,
    And the banners are folded away,
And the stress and the splendor forgotten, we know,
    Of a truth, in that judgment day,
That whatso'er else, in the Stream that rolls,
    May sink and be utterly gone,
The souls of the men who were true to their souls
        Forever go marching on!

There are those whose like, it was somehow planned,
    We never again shall see;
But I would to God there were more in the land
    As true and as simple as he,—
As he who walked in our common ways,
    With the seal of a king on his brow;
Who lived as a man among men his days,
    And belongs to the ages now!

Samuel Valentine Cole.

Included by permission of William I. Cole.

ABRAHAM LINCOLN

This man whose homely face you look upon,
  Was one of nature's masterful, great men;
Born with strong arms, that unfought battles won;
  Direct of speech, and cunning with the pen.
Chosen for large designs, he had the art
  Of winning with his humor, and he went
Straight to his mark, which was the human heart;
  Wise, too, for what he could not break, he bent.

Upon his back a more than Atlas-load,
  The burden of the Commonwealth, was laid;
He stooped, and rose up to it, though the road
  Shot suddenly downwards, not a whit dismayed.
Hold, warriors, councillors, kings! All now give place
To this dear Benefactor of the race.

                    Richard Henry Stoddard.

Included by permission of Charles Scribner's Sons.

ABRAHAM LINCOLN, THE MASTER

We need him now—his rugged faith that held
Fast to the rock of Truth through all the days
Of moil and strife, the sleepless nights; upheld
By very God was he—that God who stays
All hero-souls who will but trust in Him,
And trusting, labor as if God were not.
His eyes beheld the stars, clouds could not dim
Their glory; but his task was not forgot—
To keep his people one; to hold them true
To that fair dream their fathers willed to them—
Freedom for all; to spur them; to renew
Their hopes in bitter days; strife to condemn.
Such was his task, and well his work was done—
Who willed us greater tasks, when set his sun.

Thomas Curtis Clark.

Included by permission of the author.

ABRAHAM LINCOLN WALKS AT MIDNIGHT

It is portentous, and a thing of state
    That here at midnight, in our little town
A mourning figure walks, and will not rest,
    Near the old courthouse pacing up and down.

Or by his homestead, or in shadowed yards.
    He lingers where his children used to play,
Or through the market, on the well-worn stones
    He stalks until the dawn-stars burn away.

A bronzed, lank man! His suit of ancient black,
    A famous high-top hat and plain worn shawl
Make him the quaint great figure that men love,
    The prairie lawyer, master of us all.

He cannot sleep upon his hillside now.
    He is among us;—as in times before!
And we who toss and lie awake for long
    Breathe deep, and start, to see him pass the door.

His head is bowed. He thinks on men and kings.
    Yea, when the sick world cries, how can he sleep?
Too many peasants fight, they know not why,
    Too many homesteads in black terror weep.

The sins of all the war-lords burn his heart.
    He sees the dreadnoughts scouring every main.
He carries on his shawl-wrapped shoulders now
    The bitterness, the folly and the pain.

                 Vachel Lindsay.

From "Collected Poems" by Vachel Lindsay.
Included by permission of The Macmillan Company.

CENOTAPH OF LINCOLN

And so they buried Lincoln? Strange and vain,
　Has any creature thought of Lincoln hid
　In any vault 'neath any coffin lid,
In all the years since that wild spring of pain?
'Tis false—he never in the grave hath lain.
　You could not bury him although you slid
　Upon his clay the Cheops Pyramid,
Or heaped it with the Rocky Mountain chain,
They slew themselves;—they but set Lincoln free,
　In all the earth his great heart beats as strong,
Shall beat while pulses throb to chivalry,
　And burn with hate of tyranny and wrong,
Whoever will may find him, anywhere
Save in the tomb. Not there—he is not there.

James T. McKay.

Included by permission of Century Company.

FROM "THE GETTYSBURG ODE"

After the eyes that looked, the lips that spake
Here, from the shadows of impending death,
    Those words of solemn breath,
    What voice may fitly break
The silence doubly hallowed, left by him?
We can but bow the head, with eyes grown dim,
    And as a Nation's litany, repeat
The phrase his martyrdom hath made complete,
Noble as then, but now more sadly sweet:
"Let us, the Living, rather dedicate
Ourselves to the unfinished work, which they
Thus far advanced so nobly on its way,
    And saved the perilled State!
Let us, upon this field where they, the brave,
Their last full measure of devotion gave,
Highly resolve they have not died in vain!—
That, under God, the Nation's later birth
    Of Freedom, and the people's gain
Of their own Sovereignty, shall never wane
And perish from the circle of the earth!"
From such a perfect text, shall Song aspire
    To light her faded fire,
    And in wandering music turn
Its virtue, simple, sorrowful and stern?
His voice all elegies anticipated;
    For, whatsoe'er the strain,
    We hear that one refrain:
"We consecrate ourselves to them, the Consecrated!"

Bayard Taylor.

Included by permission of Houghton, Mifflin Company.

THE HAND OF LINCOLN

Look on this cast, and know the hand
    That bore a nation in its hold;
From this mute witness understand
    What Lincoln was—how large of mold.

The man who sped the woodman's team,
    And deepest sunk the plowman's share,
And pushed the laden raft astream,
    Of fate before him unaware.

This was the hand that knew to swing
    The axe—since thus would Freedom train
Her son—and made the forest ring,
    And drove the wedge, and toiled amain.

Firm hand, that loftier office took,
    A conscious leader's will obeyed,
And, when men sought his word and look,
    With steadfast might the gathering swayed.

No courtier's, toying with a sword,
    Nor minstrel's, laid across a lute;
A chief's, uplifted to the Lord
    When all the kings of earth were mute!

The hand of Anak, sinewed strong,
    The fingers that on greatness clutch;
Yet, lo! the marks their lines along
    Of one who strove and suffered much.

For here in knotted cord and vein,
    I trace the varying chart of years;
I know the troubled heart, the strain,
    The weight of Atlas—and the tears.

Again I see the patient brow
    That palm erewhile was wont to press;
And now 'tis furrowed deep, and now
    Made smooth with hope and tenderness.

For something of a formless grace
 This molded outline plays about;
A pitying flame, beyond our trace,
 Breathes like a spirit, in and out.

The love that casts an aureole
 Round one who, longer to endure,
Called mirth to ease his ceaseless dole,
 Yet kept his nobler purpose sure.

Lo, as I gaze, the statured man,
 Built up from yon large hand, appears;
A type that nature wills to plan
 But once in all a people's years.

What better than this voiceless cast
 To tell of such a one as he,
Since through its living semblance passed
 The thought that bade a race be free.

Edmund Clarence Stedman.

cluded by permission of Houghton, Mifflin Company.

HE LEADS US STILL

Dare we despair? Through all the nights and days
    Of lagging war he kept his courage true
Shall Doubt befog our eyes? A darker haze
    But proved the faith of him who ever knew
That Right must conquer.   May we cherish hate
    For our poor griefs, when never word nor deed
Of rancor, malice, spite, of low or great,
    In his large soul one poison drop could breed?

He leads us still.   O'er chasms yet unspanned
    Our pathway lies; the work is but begun;
But we shall do our part and leave our land
    The mightier for noble battles won.
Here Truth must triumph, Honor must prevail;
    The Nation Lincoln died for cannot fail!

Arthur Guiterman.

Revised by the author.
From "A Ballad-Maker's Pack" by Arthur Guiterman, published by
Harper Brothers. Included by permission of the author.

A HERO

He sang of joy; whate'er he knew of sadness
    He kept for his own heart's peculiar share:
So well he sang, the world imagined gladness
    To be sole tenant there.

For dreams were his, and in the dawn's fair shining,
    His spirit soared beyond the mounting lark;
But from his lips no accent of repining
    Fell when the days grew dark;

And though contending long dread Fate to master,
    He failed at last her enmity to cheat,
He turned with such a smile to face disaster
    That he sublimed defeat.

Florence Earle Coates.

Included by permission of the author and Harper Brothers.

HIS FACE

They tell you Lincoln was ungainly, plain?
    To some he seemed so; true.
Yet in his look was charm to gain
    E'en such as I, who knew
With how confirmed a will he tried
To overthrow a cause for which I would have died.

The sun may shine with naught to shroud
    Its beam, yet show less bright
Than when from out eclipsing cloud
    Its pours its radiant light;
And Lincoln, seen amid the shows of war
Clothed in his sober black, was somehow felt the more

To be a centre and a soul of power—
    An influence benign
To kindle in a faithless hour
    New trust in the divine.
Grave was his visage, but no cloud could dull
The radiance from within that made it beautiful.

A prisoner, when I saw him first—
    Wounded and sick for home—
His presence soothed my yearning's thirst
    While yet his lips were dumb;
For such compassion as his countenance wore
I had not seen nor felt in human face before.

And when, low-bending o'er his foe,
    He took in his firm hand
My wasted one, I seemed to know
    We two were of one Land;
And as my cheek flushed warm with young surprise,
God's pity looked on me from Lincoln's sorrowing eyes.

His prisoner I was from then—
    Love makes surrender sure—
And though I saw him not again,
    Some memories endure,
And I am glad my untaught worship knew
His the divinest face I ever looked into!

Florence Earle Coates.

Included by permission of the author and Harper Brothers.

HUSH'D BE THE CAMPS TO-DAY
(May 4, 1865)

Hush'd be the camps to-day,
And soldiers, let us drape our war-worn weapons,
And each with musing soul retire to celebrate
Our dear commander's death.

No more for him life's stormy conflicts,
Nor victory, nor defeat—no more time's dark events,
Charging like ceaseless clouds across the sky.

But sing, poet, in our name,
Sing of the love we bore him—because you, dweller in camps,
    know it truly.

As they invault the coffin there,
Sing—as they close the doors of earth upon him—one verse,
For the heavy hearts of soldiers.

Walt Whitman.

Included by permission of David McKay Company.

LINCOLN

Lincoln! When men would name a man,
    Just, unperturbed, magnanimous,
Tried in the lowest seat of all,
    Tried in the chief seat of the house—

Lincoln! When men would name a man
    Who wrought the great work of his age,
Who fought and fought the noblest fight,
    And marshaled it from stage to stage.

Victorious, out of dusk and dark,
    And into dawn and on till day,
Most humble when the paeans rang,
    Least rigid when the enemy lay

Prostated for his feet to tread—
    This name of Lincoln will they name,
A named revered, a name of scorn,
    Of scorn to sundry, not to fame.

Lincoln, the man who freed the slave;
    Lincoln whom never self enticed;
Slain Lincoln, worthy found to die
    A soldier of his Captain Christ.

                 Anonymous.

LINCOLN

I knew the man. I see him, as he stands
With gifts of mercy in his outstretched hands;
A kindly light within his gentle eyes,
Sad as the toil in which his heart grew wise;
His lips half-parted with the constant smile
That kindled truth, but foiled the deepest guile;
His head bent forward, and his willing ear
Divinely patient right and wrong to hear:
Great in his goodness, humble in his state,
Firm in his purpose, yet not passionate,
He led his people with a tender hand,
And won by love a sway beyond command,
Summoned by lot to mitigate a time
Frenzied by rage, unscrupulous with crime,
He bore his mission with so meek a heart
That Heaven itself took up his people's part,
And when he faltered, helped him ere he fell,
Eking his efforts out by miracle.
No King this man, by grace of God's intent;
No, something better, freeman,—President!
A nature, modeled on a higher plan,
Lord of himself, an inborn gentleman!

George Henry Boker.

From "In Praise of Lincoln" by Williams.
Included by permission of J. B. Lippincott Company.

LINCOLN

The hour was on us; where the man?
The fateful sands unfaltering ran,
    And up the way of tears
    He came into the years.

Our pastoral captain. Forth he came,
As one that answers to his name;
    Nor dreamed how high his charge,
    His work how fair and large,—

To set the stones back in the wall
Lest the divided house should fall,
    And peace from men depart,
    Hope and the childlike heart.

We looked on him; " 'Tis he," we said,
"Come crownless and unheralded,
    The shepherd who will keep
    The flocks, will fold the sheep."

Unknightly, yes; yet 'twas the mien
Presaging the immortal scene,
    Some battle of His wars
    Who sealeth up the stars.

Not he would take the past between
His hands, wipe valor's tablets clean,
    Commanding greatness wait
    Till he stand at the gate;

Not he would cramp to one small head
The awful laurels of the dead,
    Time's mighty vintage cup,
    And drink all honor up.

No flutter of the banners bold
Borne by the lusty sons of old,
    The haughty conquerors
    Set forward to their wars;

Not his their blare, their pageantries,
Their goal, their glory, was not his;
    Humbly he came to keep
    The flocks, to fold the sheep.

The need comes not without the man;
The prescient hours unceasing ran,
    And up the way of tears
    He came into the years.

Our pastoral captain, skilled to crook
The spear into the pruning hook,
    The simple, kindly man,
    Lincoln, American.

John Vance Cheney.

ncluded by permission of The Independent.

LINCOLN

FATE struck the hour!
—A crisis hour of Time.
The tocsin of a people clanging forth
Thro' the wild South and thro' the startled North
Called for a leader, master of his kind,
Fearless and firm, with clear foreseeing mind;
Who should not flinch from calumny or scorn,
Who in the depth of night could ken the morn;
Wielding a giant power
Humbly, with faith sublime.
God knew the man His sovereign grace had sealed;
God touched the man, and Lincoln stood revealed!

Jane L. Hardy.

Included by permission of The Outlook.

LINCOLN .

Would I might rouse the Lincoln in you all,
That which is gendered in the wilderness
From lonely prairies and God's tenderness.
Imperial soul, star of a weedy stream,
Born where the ghosts of buffaloes still dream,
Whose spirit hoof-beats storm above his grave,
Above that breast of earth and prairie-fire—
Fire that freed the slave.

Vachel Lindsay.

From "*The Litany of the Heroes*" in "*Collected Poems*" by *Vachel Lindsay*.
Included by permission of the author and The Macmillan Co.

LINCOLN

A peaceful life,—just toil and rest—
    All his desire;—
To read the books he liked the best
    Beside the cabin fire—
God's word and man's;—to peer sometimes
    Above the page, in smouldering gleams,
And catch, like far heroic rhymes,
    The monarch of his dreams.

A peaceful life;—to hear the low
    Of pastured herds,
Or woodman's axe that, blow on blow,
    Fell sweet as rhythmic words.
And yet there stirred within his breast
    A fateful pulse that, like a roll
Of drums, made high above his rest
    A tumult in his soul.

A peaceful life! . . . They hailed him even
    As one was hailed
Whose open palms were nailed toward Heaven
    When prayers nor aught availed.
And, lo, he paid the selfsame price
    To lull a nation's awful strife
And will us, through the sacrifice
    Of self, his peaceful life.

James Whitcomb Riley.

From "Home Folks." Copyright 1900.
Used by special permission of the publishers, The Bobbs-Merrill Co.

LINCOLN

A martyred Saint, he lies upon his bier,
While, with one heart, the kneeling nation weeps,
Until across the world the knowledge sweeps
That every sad and sacrificial tear
Waters the seed to patriot mourners dear,
That flowers in love of Country.   He who reaps
The gift of martyrdom, forever keeps
His soul in love of man, and God's own fear.
Great Prototype benign of Brotherhood—
Incarnate of the One who walked the shore
Of lonely lakes in distant Galilee;
With patient purpose undismayed he stood,
Steadfast and unafraid, and calmly bore
A Nation's Cross to a new Calvary!

Corinne Roosevelt Robinson.

Included by permission of the author and Charles Scribner's Sons.

LINCOLN LEADS

Across the page of history,
    As in a looking-glass,
Or on a moving-picture screen,
    The nation's heroes pass;
With sword and mace and pen they pace
    In epaulets and braid,
And some, with ruffles at their wrists,
    In linen fine arrayed.

But at the long procession's head,
    In loose, ill-fitting clothes,
A lanky woodsman with an axe
    Upon his shoulder goes;
In every patriotic heart
    The figure lean and tall
Is shrined beside the starry flag,
    For Lincoln leads them all.

                  Minna Irving.

THE LINCOLN STATUE
(*Gutzon Borglum, Sculptor*)

A man who drew his strength from all,
   Because of all a part;
He led with wisdom, for he knew
   The common heart.

Its hopes, it fears his eye discerned,
   And, reading, he could share.
Its griefs were his, its burdens were
   For him to bear.
Its faith that wrong must sometime yield,
   That right is ever fight,
Sustained him in the saddest hour,
   The darkest night.

In patient confidence he wrought,
   The people's will his guide,
Nor brought to his appointed task
   The touch of pride.

The people's man, familiar friend,
   Shown by the sculptor's art
As one who trusted, one who knew
   The common heart.

                              W. F. Collins.

Included by permission of the author.

LINCOLN, THE MAN OF THE PEOPLE

When the Norn Mother saw the Whirland Hour
Greatening and darkening as it hurried on,
She left the Heaven of Heroes and came down
To make a man to meet the mortal need.
She took the tried clay of the common road—
Clay warm yet with the genial heat of Earth,
Dasht through it all with a strain of prophecy;
Tempered the heap with thrill of human tears;
Then mixt a laughter with the serious stuff.
Into the shape she breathed a flame to light
That tender, tragic, ever-changing face;
And laid on him a sense of the Mystic Powers,
Moving—all husht—behind the mortal vail.
Here was a man to hold against the world,
A man to match the mountains and the sea.

The color of the ground was in him, the red earth;
The smack and tang of elemental things;
The rectitude and patience of the cliff;
The good-will of the rain that loves all leaves;
The friendly welcome of the wayside well;
The courage of the bird that dares the sea;
The gladness of the wind that shakes the corn;
The pity of the snow that hides all scars;
The secrecy of streams that make their way
Under the mountain to the rifted rock;
The tolerance and equity of light
That gives as freely to the shrinking flower
As to the great oak flaring to the wind—
To the grave's low hill as to the Matterhorn
That shoulders out the sky. Sprung from the West,
He drank the valorous youth of a new world.
The strength of virgin forests braced his mind,
The hush of spacious prairies stilled his soul,
His words were oaks in acorns; and his thoughts
Were roots that firmly gript the granite truth.

Up from log cabin to the Capitol,
One fire was on his spirit, one resolve—
To send the keen ax to the root of wrong,
Clearing a free way for the feet of God,
The eyes of conscience testing every stroke,
To make his deed the measure of a man,
He built the rail-pile as he built the State,
Pouring his splendid strength through every blow;
The grip that swung the ax in Illinois
Was on the pen that set a people free.

So came the Captain with the mighty heart;
And when the judgment thunders split the house,
Wrenching the rafters from their ancient rest,
He held the ridgepole up, and spikt again
The rafters of the Home. He held his place—
Held the long purpose like a growing tree—
Held on through blame and faltered not at praise—
Held on in calm rough-hewn sublimity,
And when he fell in whirlwind, he went down
As when a lordly cedar, green with boughs,
Goes down with a great shout upon the hills,
And leaves a lonesome place against the sky.

Edwin Markham.

Revised by the author.
Copyright 1919. *Included by permission of the author.*

THE MAN OF PEACE

What winter holiday is this?
   In Time's great calendar,
Marked with the rubric of the saints,
   And with a soldier's star,
Here stands the name of one who lived
   To serve the common weal,
With humour, tender as a prayer
   And honour firm as steel.

No hundred hundred years can dim
   The radiance of his birth,
That set unselfish laughter free
   From all the sons of earth.
Unswerved through stress and scant success,
   Out of his dreamful youth
He kept an unperverted faith
   In the almighty truth.

Born in the fulness of the days,
   Up from the teeming soil,
By the world-mother reared and schooled
   In reverence and toil,
He stands the test of all life's best
   Through play, defeat, or strain;
Never a moment was he found
   Unlovable nor vain.

Fondly we set apart this day,
   And mark this plot of earth
To be forever hallowed ground
   In honour of his birth,
Where men may come as to a shrine
   And temple of the good,
To be made sweet and strong of heart
   In Lincoln's brotherhood.

.   .   .   .   .   *Bliss Carman.*

Included by permission of the author.

THE MASTER

A flying word from here and there
Had sown the name at which we sneered,
But soon the name was everywhere,
To be reviled and then revered:
A presence to be loved and feared,
We cannot hide it, or deny
That we, the gentlemen who jeered,
May be forgotten by and by.

He came when days were perilous
And hearts of men were sore beguiled;
And having made his note of us,
He pondered and was reconciled.
Was ever master yet so mild
As he, and so untamable?
We doubted, even when he smiled,
Not knowing what he did so well.

He knew that undeceiving fate
Would shame us whom he served unsought;
He knew that he must wince and wait—
The jest of those for whom he fought;
He knew devoutly what he thought
Of us and of our ridicule;
He knew that we must all be taught
Like little children in a school.

We have a glamour to the task
That he encountered and saw through,
But little of us did he ask,
And little did we ever do.
And what appears if we review
The season when we railed and chaffed?
It is the face of one who knew
That we were learning while we laughed.

The face that in our vision feels
Again the venom that we flung,
Transfigured to the world reveals
The vigilance to which we clung.
Shrewd, hallowed, harassed, and among
The mysteries that are retold,
The face we see was ever young,
Nor could it ever have been old.

For he, to whom we have applied
Our shopman's test of age and worth,
Was elemental when he died,
As he was ancient at his birth:
The saddest among kings of earth,
Bowed with a galling crown, this man
Met rancor with a crytic mirth,
Laconic—and Olympian.

The love, the grandeur, and the fame
Are bounded by the world alone;
The calm, the smouldering, and the flame
Of awful patience were his own:
With him they are forever flown
Past all our fond self-shadowings,
Wherewith we cumber the Unknown
As with inept Icarian wings.

For we were not as other men:
'Twas ours to soar and his to see.
But we are coming down again,
And we shall come down pleasantly;
Nor shall we longer disagree
On what it is to be sublime,
But flourish in our perigee
And have one Titan at a time.

Edwin Arlington Robinson.

Included by permission of the author and Charles Scribner's Sons.

NANCY HANKS

Prairie child,
    Brief as dew,
What winds of wonder
    Nourished you?

Rolling plains
    Of billowy green;
Far horizons,
    Blue, serene;

Lofty skies
    The slow clouds climb,
Where burning stars
    Beat out the time:

These, and the dreams
    Of fathers bold—
Baffled longings,
    Hopes untold—

Gave to you
    A heart of fire,
Love like deep waters,
    Brave desire.

Ah, when youth's rapture
    Went out in pain,
And all seemed over,
    Was all in vain?

O soul obscure,
    Whose wings life bound,
And soft death folded
    Under the ground.

Wilding lady,
    Still and true,
Who gave us Lincoln
    And never knew:

To you at last
     Our praise, our tears,
Love and a song
     Through the nation's years.

Mother of Lincoln,
     Our tears, our praise;
A battle-flag
     And the victor's bays!

                         Harriet Monroe.

Revised by the author.
Included by permission of the author and The Macmillan Company.

O CAPTAIN! MY CAPTAIN

O Captain! my Captain! our fearful trip is done,
The ship has weather'd every rack, the prize we sought is won,
The port is near, the bells I hear, the people all exulting,
While follow eyes the steady keel, the vessel grim and daring;
    But O heart! heart! heart!
        O the bleeding drops of blood,
           Where on the deck my Captain lies,
           Fallen cold and dead.

O Captain! my Captain! rise up and hear the bells;
Rise up—for you the flag is flung—for you the bugle trills.
For you bouquets and ribbon'd wreaths—for you the shores
    a-crowding,
For you they call, the swaying mass, their eager faces turning;
    Here, Captain! dear father!
        This arm beneath your head!
           It is some dream that on the deck,
           You've fallen cold and dead.

My Captain does not answer, his lips are pale and still,
My father does not feel my arm, he has no pulse nor will,
The ship is anchor'd safe and sound, its voyage closed and
    done,
From fearful trip the victor comes in with object won;
    Exult, O shores, and ring, O bells!
        But I with mournful tread,
           Walk the deck my Captain lies,
           Fallen cold and dead.
                  Walt Whitman.

Included by permission of David McKay Company.

ON A BUST OF LINCOLN

This was a man of mighty mould
    Who walked erewhile our earthly ways,
Fashioned as leaders were of old
    In the heroic days!

Mark how austere the rugged height
    Of brow—a will not wrought to bend
Yet in the eyes behold the light
    That made the foe a friend!

Sagacious he beyond the test
    Of quibbling schools that praise or ban;
Supreme in all the broadest, best,
    We hail American.

When bronze is but as ash to flame,
    And marble but as wind-blown chaff,
Still shall the lustre of his name
    Stand as his cenotaph!

Clinton Scollard.

Included by permission of the author.

OUR MARTYR-CHIEF

Such was he, our Martyr-Chief,
    Whom late the Nation he had led,
    With ashes on her head,
Wept with the passion of an angry grief:
Forgive me, if from present things I turn
To speak what in my heart will beat and burn,
And hang my wreath on his world-honored urn.
    Nature, they say, doth dote,
    And cannot make a man
    Save on some worn-out plan,
    Repeating up by rote;
For him her Old World moulds aside she threw,
    And, choosing sweet clay from the breast
    Of the unexhausted West,
With stuff untainted shaped a hero new,
Wise, steadfast in the strength of God, and true.
    How beautiful to see,
Once more a shepherd of mankind indeed,
Who loved his charge, but never loved to lead;
One whose meek flock the people joyed to be,
    Not lured by any cheat of birth,
    But by his clear-grained human worth,
And brave old wisdom of sincerity!
    They knew that outward grace is dust;
    They could not choose but trust
In the sure-footed mind's unfaltering skill,
    And supple-tempered will
That bent like perfect steel to spring again and thrust.
    His was no lonely mountain-peak of mind,
Thrusting to thin air o'er our cloudy bars,
    A sea-mark now, now lost in vapors blind;
    Broad prairie rather, genial, level-lined,
    Fruitful and friendly for all human kind,
Yet also nigh to heaven and loved of loftiest stars.

Great captains, with their guns and drums,
Disturb our judgment for the hour,
But at last silence comes;
These all are gone, and standing like a tower,
Our children shall behold his fame,
The kindly-earnest, brave, foreseeing man,
Sagacious, patient, dreading praise, not blame,
New birth of our new soil, the first American.

James Russell Lowell.

Included by permission of Houghton, Mifflin Company.

PRESIDENT LINCOLN'S GRAVE

Lay his dear ashes where ye will,—
On southern slope or western hill;
And build above his sacred name
Your proudest monument of fame;
Yet still his grave our hearts shall be;
His monument a people free!
    Sing sweet, sing low!
    We loved him so!
His grave a nation's heart shall be,
His monument a people free!

Wave, prairie winds! above his sleep
Your mournful dirges, long and deep;
Proud marble! o'er his virtues raise
The tribute of your glittering praise;
Yet still his grave our hearts shall be;
His monument a people free!
    Sing sweet, sing low;
    We loved him so!
His grave a nation's heart shall be;
His monument a people free!

So just, so merciful, so wise,
Ye well may shrine him where he lies;
So simply good, so great the while
Ye well may praise the marble pile;
Yet still his grave our hearts shall be;
His monument a people free!
    Sing sweet, sing low;
    We loved him so!
His grave a nation's heart shall be;
His monument a people free!

Caroline A. Mason.

TO BORGLUM'S SEATED STATUE OF
ABRAHAM LINCOLN

Alone, upon the broad low bench, he sits,
From carping foes and friends alike withdrawn;
With tragic patience for the spirit dawn
He waits, yet through the deep-set eyes hope flits
As he the back unto the burden fits.
Within this rugged man of brains and brawn
The quiv'ring nation's high powered currents drawn,
As waves of love and kindness he transmits.

O prairie poet, prophet, children's friend!
Great-brained, great-willed, great-hearted man and true,
May we, like thee, in prayerful patience plod
With courage toward the wished for, peaceful end!
May we thy helpful friendliness renew,
Thou war worn soul communing with thy God!

Charlotte B. Jordan.

Included by permission of the Sun.

TO THE MEMORY OF ABRAHAM LINCOLN
(1865)

O, slow to smite and swift to spare,
    Gentle and merciful and just!
Who, in the fear of God, didst bear
    The sword of power—a nation's trust.

In sorrow by thy bier we stand,
    Amid the awe that hushes all,
And speak the anguish of a land
    That shook with horror at thy fall.

Thy task is done—the bond are free;
    We bear thee to an honored grave,
Whose noblest monument shall be
    The broken fetters of the slave.

Pure was thy life; its bloody close
    Hath placed thee with the sons of light,
Among the noble host of those
    Who perished in the cause of right.

William Cullen Bryant.

From the "Collected Works" by William Cullen Bryant.
Included by permission of D. Appleton & Company.

TOLLING
(April 15, 1865)

Tolling, tolling, tolling!
    All the bells of the land!
Lo, the patriot martyr
    Taketh his journey grand!
Travels into the ages,
    Bearing a hope how dear!
Into life's unknown vistas,
    Liberty's great pioneer.

Tolling, tolling, tolling!
    See, they come as a cloud,
Hearts of a mighty people,
    Bearing his pall and shroud.
Lifting up, like a banner,
    Signals of loss and woe;
Wonder of breathless nations,
    Moveth a solemn show.

Tolling, tolling, tolling!
    Was it, O man beloved,
Was it thy funeral only
    Over the land that moved?
Veiled by that hour of anguish,
    Borne into the rebel rout,
Forth into utter darkness,
    Slavery's curse went out.

Lucy Larcom.

Included by permission of Houghton, Mifflin Company.

YOUNG LINCOLN

Men saw no portents on that night
A hundred years ago. No omens flared
Above that rail-built cabin with one door,
And windowless to all the peering stars.
They laid him in the hollow of a log,
Humblest of cradles, save that other one—
The manger in the stall at Bethlehem.

No portents! yet with whisper and alarm
The Evil Powers that dread the nearing feet
Of heroes held a council in that hour;
And sent three fates to darken that low door
To baffle and beat back the heaven-sent child.
Three were the fates—gaunt Poverty that chains,
Gray Drudgery that grinds the hope away,
And gaping Ignorance that starves the soul.

They came with secret laughters to destroy.
Ever they dogged him, counting every step,
Waylaid his youth and struggled for his life.
They came to master, but he made them serve.
And from the wrestle with the destinies,
He rose with all his energies aglow.

For God, upon whose steadfast shoulders rest
These governments of ours, had not forgot.
He needed for His purposes a voice,
A voice to be a clarion on the wind,
Crying the word of freedom to dead hearts,
The word the centuries had waited for.

So hidden in the West, God shaped His man.
There in the unspoiled solitudes he grew,
Unwarped by culture and uncramped by creed;
Keeping his course courageous and alone,
As goes the Mississippi to the sea.
His daring spirit burst the narrow bounds,
Rose resolute; and like the sea-called stream,
He tore new channels where he found no way.

The tools were his first teachers, sternly kind.
The plow, the scythe, the maul, the echoing axe,
Taught him their homely wisdom and their peace.
He had the plain man's genius—common sense,
Yet rage for knowledge drove his mind afar;
He fed his spirit with the bread of books,
And slaked his thirst at all the wells of thought.

But most he read the heart of common man,
Scanned all its secret pages stained with tears,
Saw all the guile, saw all the piteous pain;
And yet could keep the smile about his lips,
Love and forgive, see all and pardon all;
His only fault, the fault that some of old
Laid even on God—that he was ever wont
To bend the law to let his mercy out.

Edwin Markham.

Revised by the author.
Included by permission of the author.

AN ADDITIONAL LIST OF POEMS WITH SOURCES

The following is an addition list of poems which it has not been possible to include in this volume. Some of the poems are to be found in sources other than those given.

WASHINGTON

Great Washington   *Annette Wynne*
   In "For Days and Days"

Lines   *William Cullen Bryant*
   In "Washington's Birthday"
A Little Boy and a Cherry Tree
   In "For Days and Days"

The Minuet   *Mary Mapes Dodge*
   In "Along the Path"

Washington   *Robert Bridges*
   In "For Days and Days"

Washington   *William Cullen Bryant*
   In "Washington's Birthday"
Washington   *Annette Wynne*
   In "For Days and Days"

Washington   *Will Carleton*
   In "Washington's Birthday"

Washington at Trenton   *Richard Watson Gilder*
   In "Poems of American History"

Washington's Birthday   *Margaret E. Sangster*
   In "Washington's Birthday"

Washington's Monument   *Walt Whitman*
   In "Leaves of Grass"

Washington's Name in the Hall of
      fame   *Margaret E. Sangster*
   In "Washington's Birthday"

When Our Land Was New   *Annette Wynne*
   In "For Days and Days"